Raintree is an imprint of Capstone Global Library Limited,
a company incorporated in England and Wales having its
registered office at 7 Pilgrim Street, London, EC4V 6LB –
Registered company number: 6695582

www.raintreepublishers.co.uk
myorders@raintreepublishers.co.uk

First published by Stone Arch Books © 2013
First published in the United Kingdom in 2014
The moral rights of the proprietor have been asserted

Originally published by DC Comics in
the US in single magazine form as
Batman: The Brave and the Bold #7.
Copyright © 2013 DC Comics. All Rights Reserved.

Ashley C. Andersen Zantop Publisher
Michael Dahl Editorial Director
Donald Lemke & Sean Tulien Editors
Heather Kindseth Creative Director
Hilary Wacholz Designer
Kathy McColley Production Specialist

DC COMICS
Rachel Gluckstern & Michael Siglain Original US Editors
Harvey Richards US Assistant Editor

ISBN 978 1 406 26651 1
17 16 15 14 13
10 9 8 7 6 5 4 3 2 1

Printed and bound in China by Leo Paper Products Ltd

British Library Cataloguing in Publication Data
A full catalogue record for this book is available from the British Library

BATMAN

THE BRAVE AND THE BOLD®

THE SECRET OF THE DOOMSDAY DESIGN!

J. TORRES .... WRITER
J. BONE .... PENCILLER
J. BONE .... INKER
HEROIC AGE .... COLOURIST
TRAVIS LANHAM .... LETTERER
SCOTT JERALDS .... COVER ARTIST

SOON...

...AN ABANDONED CLOTHING FACTORY IN THE OLD GARMENT DISTRICT? ARE YOU *SURE* YOU'VE GOT THIS RIGHT?

carnaby clothing co.

YEAH, BATMAN! I TRACKED *ELASTI-GIRL'S* SCENT TO THIS PLACE!

UH... BATMAN? I THINK THAT *MANNEQUIN* OVER THERE JUST... MOVED?

THEY'RE *ALL* ON THE MOVE!

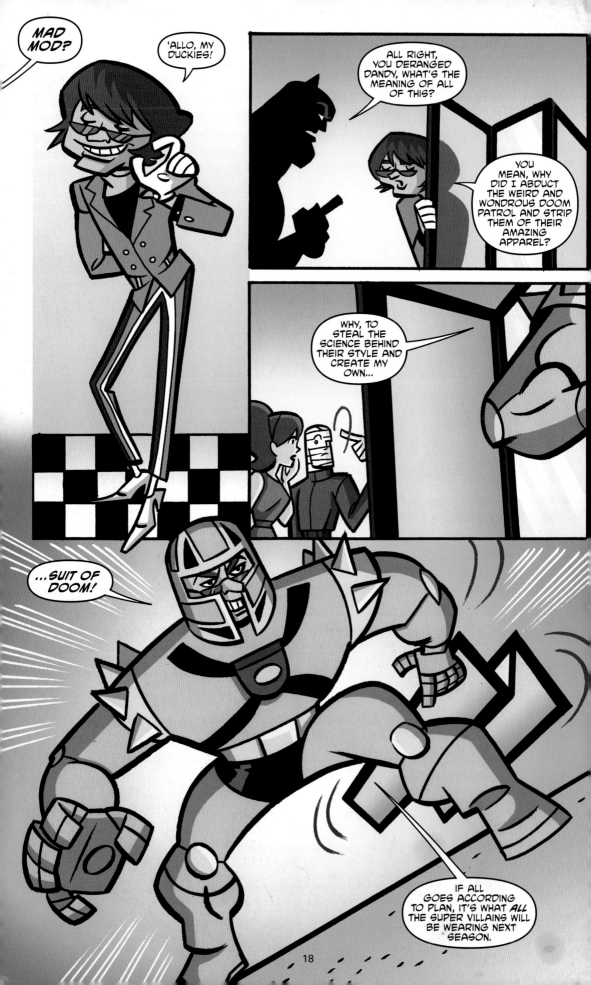

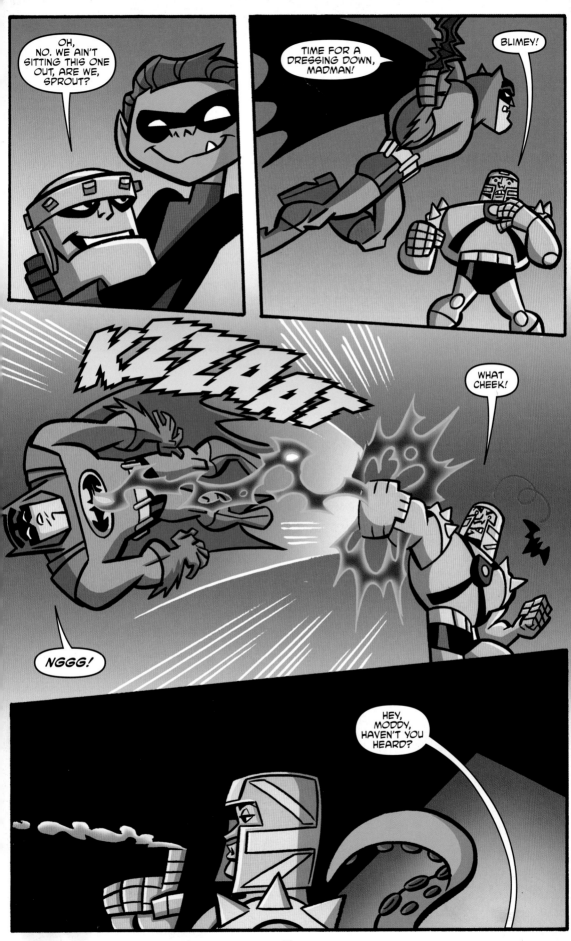

MAD MOD

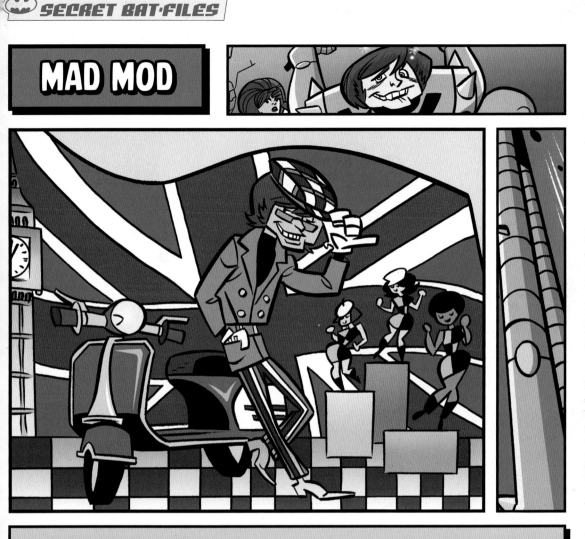

Mad Mod is a former fashion designer with a fabulous sense of style but not the good sense to use his talents for good instead of evil. He may be the best-dressed super-villain in history, but history also shows he's the worst at getting away with his crimes.

TOP SECRET:
Mad Mod first faced off against the Teen Titans and to this day has his design on their demise.

DOOM PATROL

The Doom Patol are: former racing car driver now the steel sentinel Robotman, former Hollywood actress now the size-shifting Elasti-Girl, former test pilot now the Radioactive Man, and former orphan now the shape-shifting Beast Boy, led by Dr Niles "The Chief" Caulder. The Doom Patrol often battles evil in the form of villains and monsters as strange and weird as they are.

TOP SECRET:
Each member of the team revived their powers after tragic accidents, but they have overcome their tragedy to help others in trouble.

CREATORS

J. TORRES WRITER

J. Torres won the Shuster Award for Outstanding Writer for his work on *Batman: Legends of the Dark Knight*, *Love As a Foreign Language*, and *Teen Titans Go*. He is also the writer of the Eisner Award nominated *Alison Dare* and the YALSA listed *Days Like This* and *Lola: A Ghost Story*. Other comic book credits include *Avatar: The Last Airbender*, *Legion of Super-Heroes in the 31st Century*, *Ninja Scroll*, *Wonder Girl*, *Wonder Woman*, and *WALL·E: Recharge*.

J. BONE ILLUSTRATOR

J. Bone is a Toronto-based illustrator and comic book artist. Besides *DC Super Friends*, he has worked on comic books such as *Spiderman: Tangled Web*, *Mr. Gum*, *Gotham Girls*, and *Madman Adventures*. He is also the co-creator of the Alison Dare comic book series.

GLOSSARY

abandoned left forever

captive person or an animal that has been taken prisoner

deranged insane

legendary something from a legend, or story handed down from earlier times. Legends are often based on fact, but they are not entirely true.

literally exactly how it is said or written

radioactive giving off harmful radiation

sorcery art of using magical spells and incantations

unveil reveal or disclose

VISUAL QUESTIONS & PROMPTS

1. In the panel below, Batman and Beast Boy are sneaking up to a building. Why do you think the artists included a smaller, circular panel on top of the bottom one? How does it help you understand what's going on in the story?

2. Why do you think Negative Man's speech balloons are different from everyone else's? Why do you think the artists chose to draw them that way?

3. Why do the speech balloons in the panel below have jagged tails? Why do you think the artists chose to draw them that way?

4. Beast Boy can shapeshift into any animal he desires. How does this ability help him solve problems in this comic book? What are some other animal forms that might come in handy for fighting crime?

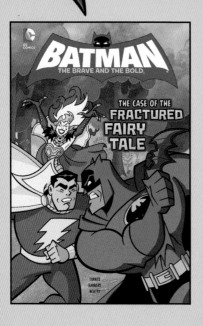